Look at Me, I'm Learning French

(A STORY FOR AGES 3-6)

By Daniel Williamson

Illustrated by Kleverton Monteiro

DW

First published in 2019 by Daniel Williamson
www.danielwilliamson.co.uk
This edition published in 2020
Text © Daniel Williamson 2019
Illustrations © Kleverton Monteiro 2019
Cover design © by Uzuri Designs 2019

ISBN 978-1-9162563-1-6

This book is dedicated
to my daughter
Carmela

I'm a small person in a big, big world!

Je suis une petite personne
dans un grand, grand monde !

I know people bigger than me.
Bigger people know more things because
they start to learn when they are small.

Je connais des gens plus grands que moi. Les gens
plus grands savent plus de choses parce qu'ils
commencent à apprendre quand ils sont petits.

Not everyone speaks English like me. Some bigger people speak French, some speak two languages!

Tout le monde ne parle pas anglais comme moi. Certaines personnes plus grandes parlent français, d'autres parlent deux langues !

I want to learn French too so I can speak to French speaking people and make even more friends!

Je veux apprendre le français aussi, pour pouvoir parler avec des gens qui parlent français et me faire encore plus d'amis !

First I'm going to learn to count using the peas on my plate.

D'abord, je vais apprendre à compter en
utilisant les pois dans mon assiette.

ONE
UN

TWO
DEUX

THREE
TROIS

FOUR
QUATRE

FIVE
CINQ

SIX
SIX

SEVEN
SEPT

EIGHT
HUIT

NINE
NEUF

TEN
DIX

Now I know how to count to ten! Look at me
I'm learning French, learning French is Fun!

Maintenant, je sais compter jusqu'à dix !
Regarde-moi, j'apprends le français,
apprendre le français, c'est amusant !

I wonder what to say if I meet a French person?
I think I would say - "Hello, how are you?" Then
they would say - "I'm fine thanks and you?"

Je me demande quoi dire si je rencontre une personne
française ? Je pense que je dirais : « Bonjour, comment
vas-tu ? Puis ils diraient : – Ça va, et toi ? »

Then I would need to tell them my name. I would say –
"Hello, my name is _____, what's your name?"

Alors j'aurais besoin de leur dire mon nom. Je dirais :
« Bonjour, mon nom est _____, quel est ton nom ? »

Now I want to tell them my age and ask how old they are. Let's see if I can remember the numbers!

Maintenant, je veux leur dire mon âge et leur demander quel âge ils ont. Voyons si je me souviens des chiffres !

I am _____ years old, how old are you?

J'ai _____ ans, quel âge as-tu ?

Look at me I'm learning French!
Learning French is fun!

Regarde-moi, j'apprends le français!
Apprendre le français, c'est amusant!

I need to know how to say the things I like and the things I don't like, let's try some sentences!

J'ai besoin de savoir comment dire les choses que j'aime et les choses que je n'aime pas, essayons quelques phrases !

I like sunny days. I like to go to the park
and play on the slide and swings!

J'aime les journées ensoleillées. J'aime aller au
parc et jouer sur le toboggan et les balançoires !

I also love playing with my friends outside.
Sometimes we play football,
sometimes we play hide and seek!

J'aime aussi jouer avec mes amis à l'extérieur.
Parfois, nous jouons au football,
parfois nous jouons à cache-cache !

I don't like when it's rainy and windy so I go to the cinema, watch cartoons and eat popcorn.

Je n'aime pas quand il pleut et qu'il y a du vent, alors je vais au cinéma, je regarde des dessins animés et je mange du pop-corn.

My favourite thing to do is go for a picnic.
I like eating apple slices but I prefer bananas!

Ma chose préférée est d'aller faire un pique-nique.
J'aime manger les tranches de pomme,
mais je préfère les bananes !

Last time I went to the park I saw a huge rainbow.
Let's see if I can remember all the colours!

La dernière fois que je suis allé au parc, j'ai vu un
énorme arc-en-ciel. Voyons si je me souviens de
toutes les couleurs !

RED   ROUGE

ORANGE   ORANGE

YELLOW   JAUNE

GREEN   VERT

BLUE   BLEU

INDIGO   INDIGO

VIOLET   VIOLET

The colours of the rainbow are red, orange, yellow, green, blue, indigo and violet!

Les couleurs de l'arc-en-ciel sont le rouge, l'orange, le jaune, le vert, le bleu, l'indigo et le violet !

Look at me I'm learning French!
Learning French is fun!!!

Regarde-moi, j'apprends le français !
Apprendre le français, c'est amusant !

At home I have some different pets and they are different colours too! I have a brown dog, a black and white cat and a grey rabbit.

À la maison, j'ai différents animaux de compagnie et ils sont des couleurs différentes aussi ! J'ai un chien brun, un chat noir et blanc et un lapin gris.

My dog likes me to throw his ball for him, he always brings it back, it's his favourite game!

Mon chien aime que je lui lance sa balle, il la ramène toujours, c'est son jeu préféré !

My cat likes to sleep on the sofa all day,
he's a very lazy cat!

Mon chat aime dormir sur le canapé toute
la journée, c'est un chat très paresseux !

My rabbit lives in the garden, he eats carrots all day, they help him see better at night time!

Mon lapin vit dans le jardin, il mange des carottes toute la journée, elles l'aident à mieux voir la nuit !

At night time I get into my pyjamas, I love getting into bed for a story, then I close my eyes and slowly fall asleep, ready to learn more French tomorrow...

La nuit, je me mets en pyjama, j'aime me coucher pour une histoire, puis je ferme les yeux et je m'endors lentement, prêt à apprendre plus de français demain...

This author has developed a bilingual book series designed to introduce children to a number of new languages from a very young age.

If you enjoyed reading this story, you will undoubtedly like popular rhyming picture books from this author which are also currently available.

Message from the Author

I'd like to say a massive thank you to every single child and adult that read one of my books! My dream is to bring cultures together through fun illustrations, imagination and creativity via the power of books.

If you would like to join me on this journey, please visit my website danielwilliamson.co.uk where each email subscriber receives a free ebook to keep or we will happily send to a friend of your choice as a gift!

Nothing makes me happier than a review on the platform you purchased my book telling me where my readers are from! Also, please click on my links below and follow me to join my ever-growing online family! Remember there is no time like the present and the present is a gift!

Yours gratefully

Daniel Williamson

@DanWAuthor

@danwauthor

@DanWAuthor

CPSIA information can be obtained
at www.ICGtesting.com
Printed in the USA
LVHW070851200222
711561LV00008B/222

9 781916 256316